Calendar 2022

January

M	T	W	T	F	S	S
					1	2
3	4	5	6	7	8	9
10	11	12	13	14	15	16
17	18	19	20	21	22	23
24	25	26	27	28	29	30
31						

February

M	T	W	T	F	S	S
	1	2	3	4	5	6
7	8	9	10	11	12	13
14	15	16	17	18	19	20
21	22	23	24	25	26	27
28						

March

M	T	W	T			
	1	2	3			
7	8	9	10	11	12	13
14	15	16	17	18	19	20
21	22	23	24	25	26	27
28	29	30	31			

						S
						3
4	5	6	7	8	9	10
11	12	13	14	15	16	17
18	19	20	21	22	23	24
25	26	27	28	29	30	

May

M	T	W	T	F	S	S
						1
2	3	4	5	6	7	8
9	10	11	12	13	14	15
16	17	18	19	20	21	22
23	24	25	26	27	28	29
30	31					

June

M	T	W	T	F	S	S
		1	2	3	4	5
6	7	8	9	10	11	12
13	14	15	16	17	18	19
20	21	22	23	24	25	26
27	28	29	30			

July

M	T	W	T	F	S	S
				1	2	3
4	5	6	7	8	9	10
11	12	13	14	15	16	17
18	19	20	21	22	23	24
25	26	27	28	29	30	31

August

M	T	W	T	F	S	S
1	2	3	4	5	6	7
8	9	10	11	12	13	14
15	16	17	18	19	20	21
22	23	24	25	26	27	28
29	30	31				

September

M	T	W	T	F	S	S
			1	2	3	4
5	6	7	8	9	10	11
12	13	14	15	16	17	18
19	20	21	22	23	24	25
26	27	28	29	30		

October

M	T	W	T	F	S	S
					1	2
3	4	5	6	7	8	9
10	11	12	13	14	15	16
17	18	19	20	21	22	23
24	25	26	27	28	29	30
31						

November

M	T	W	T	F	S	S
	1	2	3	4	5	6
7	8	9	10	11	12	13
14	15	16	17	18	19	20
21	22	23	24	25	26	27
28	29	30				

December

M	T	W	T	F	S	S
			1	2	3	4
5	6	7	8	9	10	11
12	13	14	15	16	17	18
19	20	21	22	23	24	25
26	27	28	29	30	31	

‘Every tree in the wood was frost-sprinkled and sparkling, and frozen puddles creaked and crackled under Fletcher’s paws.’

– Fletcher and the Snowflake Christmas

January 2022

Monday	Tuesday	Wednesday	Thursday	Friday	Saturday	Sunday
27	28	29	30	31	1 New Year’s Day	2
3 Bank Holiday	4	5	6	7	8	9
10	11	12	13	14	15	16
17	18	19	20	21	22	23
24	25 St. Dwynwen’s Day	26	27	28	29	30
31	1	2	3	4	5	6

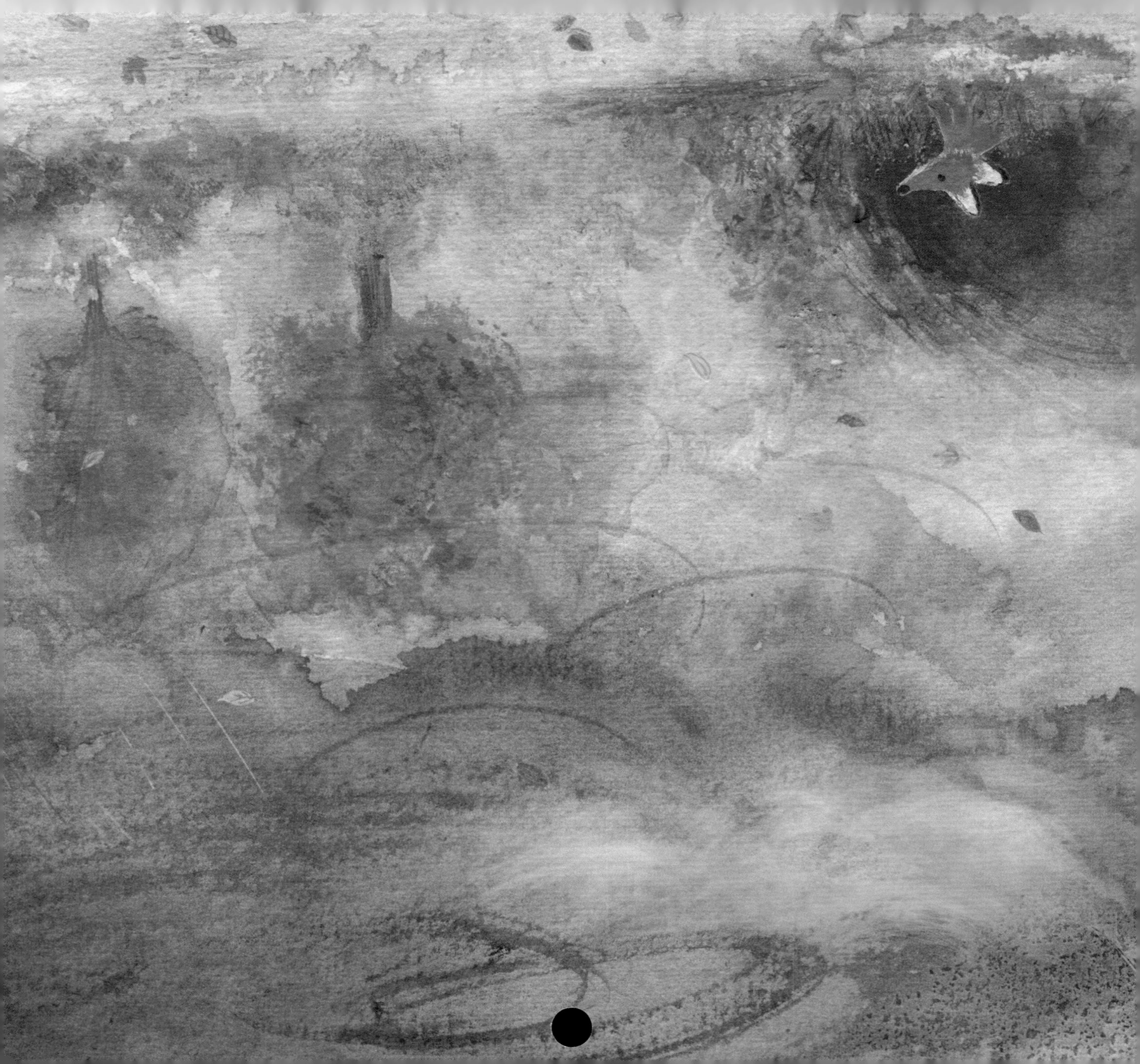

‘Leaves were whirling through the sodden wood. Rainclouds were racing across the stormy sky. The wind ripped the clouds apart, the sun came shining through...’

– Fletcher and the Rainbow

February 2022

Monday	Tuesday	Wednesday	Thursday	Friday	Saturday	Sunday
31	1	2	3	4	5	6
7	8	9	10	11	12	13
14 Valentine's Day	15	16	17	18	19	20
21	22	23	24	25	26	27
28	1	2	3	4	5	6
7	8	9	10	11	12	13

'Instead of the bright, rich green of spring, the ground was covered in drifts of white, and when a soft breeze danced through the branches it carried snowy flakes.'

– Fletcher and the Springtime Blossom

March 2022

Monday	Tuesday	Wednesday	Thursday	Friday	Saturday	Sunday
28	1 St. David's Day	2	3	4	5	6
7	8	9	10	11	12	13
14	15	16	17 St. Patrick's Day	18	19	20
21	22	23	24	25	26	27 Mothering Sunday British Summertime begins
28	29	30	31	1	2	3
4	5	6	7	8	9	10

‘The wood was full of the chirruping, bustling, sing-song sounds of spring. Fletcher bounced along with his nose in the air, sniffing the just-burst buds of flowers and playing chase with butterflies.’

– Fletcher and the Springtime Blossom

April 2022

Monday	Tuesday	Wednesday	Thursday	Friday	Saturday	Sunday
28	29	30	31	1	2	3
4	5	6	7	8	9	10
11	12	13	14	15 Good Friday	16	17 Easter Sunday
18 Easter Monday	19	20	21	22	23	24
25 St. George’s Day	26	27	28	29	30	1
2	3	4	5	6	7	8

‘The trees were stretching in the sun, their branches bright with raindrops. Buds were swelling. Petals were unfurling. Everything in the wood was growing... except one juicy green leaf...’

– Fletcher and the Caterpillar

May 2022

Monday	Tuesday	Wednesday	Thursday	Friday	Saturday	Sunday
25	26	27	28	29	30	1
2 May Day Bank Holiday	3	4	5	6	7	8
9	10	11	12	13	14	15
16	17	18	19	20	21	22
23	24	25	26	27	28	29
30	31	1	2	3	4	5

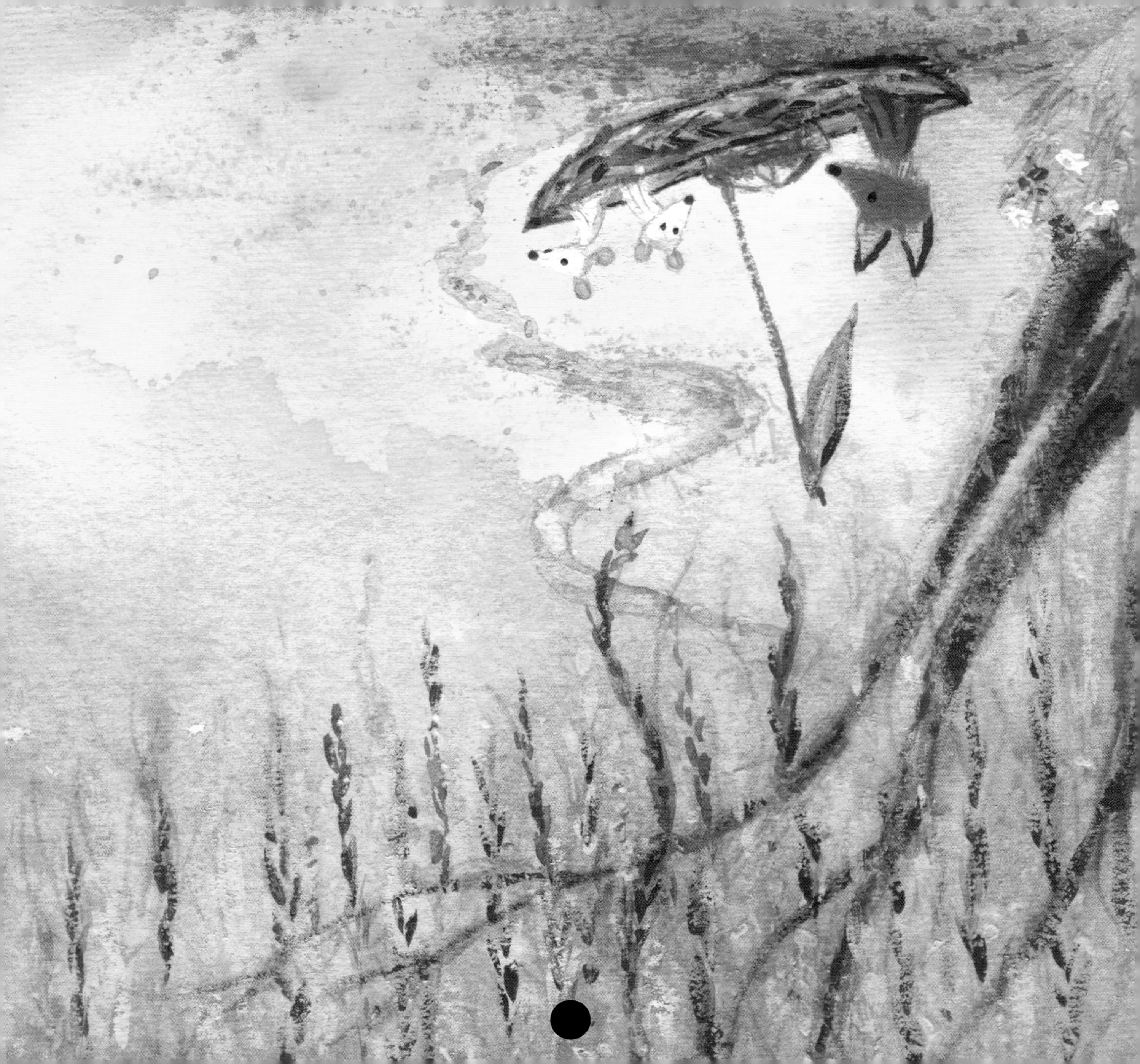

'Fletcher waited patiently through the endless days. The gurgling stream slowed to a trickle, the rich earth turned to dust and the leaves hung heavy on the trees.'

– Fletcher and the Caterpillar

June 2022

Monday	Tuesday	Wednesday	Thursday	Friday	Saturday	Sunday
30	31	1	2 Whitsun Bank Holiday	3 Platinum Jubilee Bank Holiday	4	5
6	7	8	9	10	11	12
13	14	15	16	17	18	19 Father's Day
20	21	22	23	24	25	26
27	28	29	30	1	2	3
4	5	6	7	8	9	10

'Little by little, a golden shaft of sunlight crept over them... so when he woke, Fletcher felt as though he was spotlit on a stage.'

– Fletcher and the Summer Show

July 2022

Monday	Tuesday	Wednesday	Thursday	Friday	Saturday	Sunday
27	28	29	30	1	2	3
4	5	6	7	8	9	10
11	12	13	14	15	16	17
18	19	20	21	22	23	24
25	26	27	28	29	30	31
1	2	3	4	5	6	7

'The frogs were croaking in their pond, deep in a shady glade. Fletcher crouched down and asked them to teach Rabbit to croak.'

– Fletcher and the Summer Show

August 2022

Monday	Tuesday	Wednesday	Thursday	Friday	Saturday	Sunday
1	2	3	4	5	6	7
8	9	10	11	12	13	14
15	16	17	18	19	20	21
22	23	24	25	26	27	28
29 Summer Bank Holiday	30	31	1	2	3	4
5	6	7	8	9	10	11

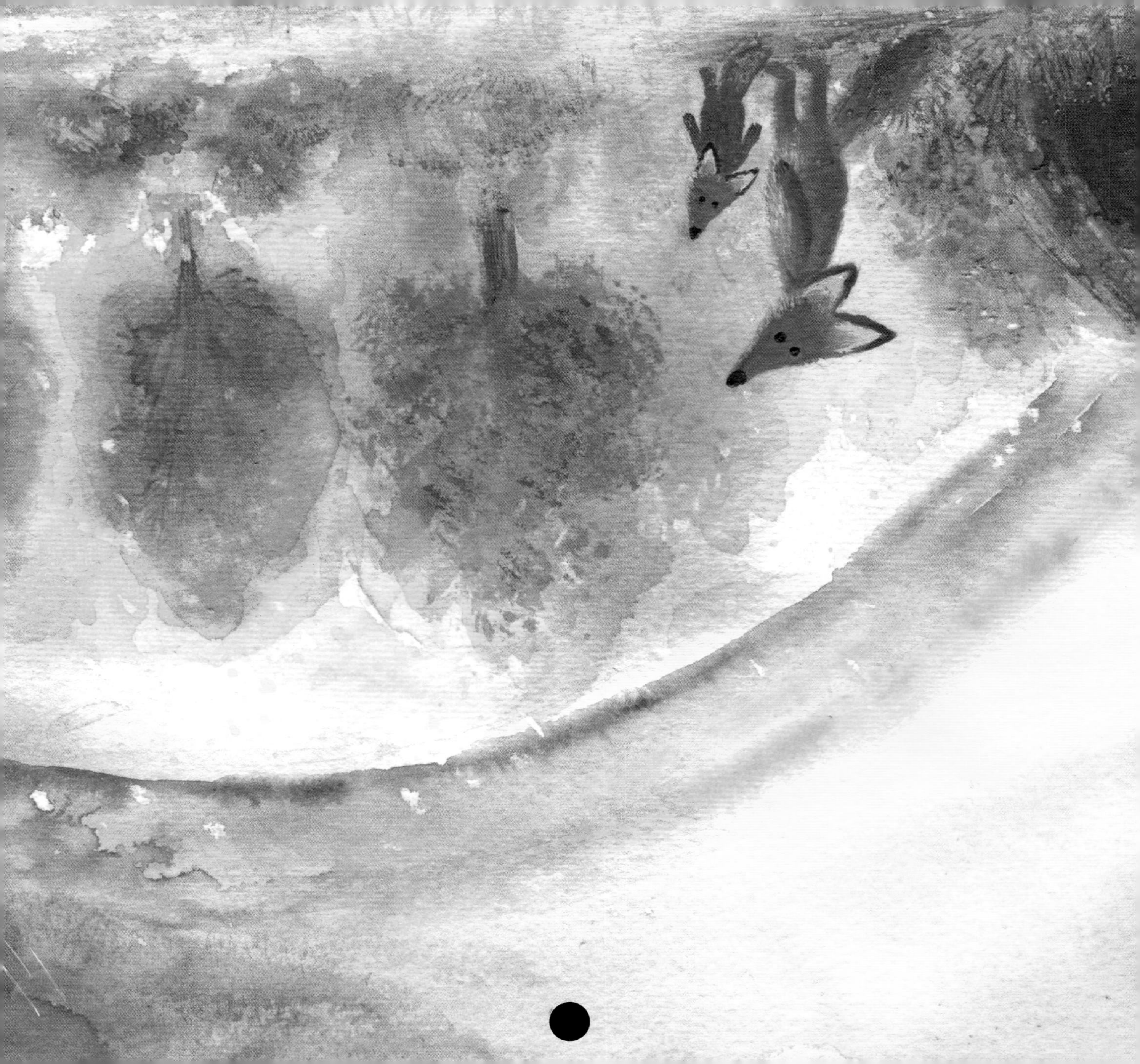

'Fletcher gazed at the arc of colour lighting up the sky. Maybe, if he could find it, he could help it shine forever.'

– Fletcher and the Rainbow

September 2022

Monday	Tuesday	Wednesday	Thursday	Friday	Saturday	Sunday
29	30	31	1	2	3	4
5	6	7	8	9	10	11
12	13	14	15	16	17	18
19	20	21	22	23	24	25
26	27	28	29	30	1	2
3	4	5	6	7	8	9

'One day, as Fletcher sat under the tree, the wind began to blow. A small, brown leaf blew off the tree and drifted towards the ground. Fletcher jumped up and caught it, very gently, in his paw.'

– Fletcher and the Falling Leaves

October 2022

Monday	Tuesday	Wednesday	Thursday	Friday	Saturday	Sunday
26	27	28	29	30	1	2
3	4	5	6	7	8	9
10	11	12	13	14	15	16
17	18	19	20	21	22	23
24	25	26	27	28	29	30 British Summertime ends
31	1	2	3	4	5	6

'They tossed and turned and twitched and twirled and tumbled to the ground. They brushed Fletcher's ears and nose and filled his dreams with a whispering sound.'

– Fletcher and the Falling Leaves

November 2022

Monday	Tuesday	Wednesday	Thursday	Friday	Saturday	Sunday
31	1	2	3	4	5	6
7	8	9	10	11	12	13
14	15	16	17	18	19	20
21	22	23	24	25	26	27
28	29	30 St. Andrew's Day	1	2	3	4
5	6	7	8	9	10	11